SPORTS
AND GAMES

D0785574

SPY

Introduction

In some sports, individual strength, speed, stamina, or skill are tested. In other sports, such as cricket or football, the qualities of leadership and teamwork are vital for success. And, field events, like throwing the javelin, obviously have their origins in competitions where the prowess of a warrior could be put to the test. However sports and games developed, there seems no doubt that humans have competed in this way for thousands of years, since the first time two individuals tried to find out who could throw a stone further, or since teams of horsemen played a primitive kind of Polo using inflated animal skins and makeshift mallets.

Nowadays, as well as being played at schools and universities or among friends at a leisure centre, sports and games are big business with huge amounts of money at stake for sponsors and players alike. Sport is exciting and colourful, with crowds of spectators cheering on their heroes or following their teams around the world to watch them compete.

As well as great spectacles, many sports can give long term health benefits to the participants. If you can find a sport you enjoy when growing up this is a great way to keep fit.

How to use your I-SPY book

As you work through this book, you will notice that the subjects are arranged in groups relating to where you will find the activities. You need 1000 points to send off for your I-Spy certificate (see page 64) but that is not too difficult because there are masses of points in every book. As you make each I-Spy, write your score in the box and, where there is a question, double your score if you can answer it. Check your answer against the correct one on page 63. You can achieve your I-Spy score for each sport by spotting it on television but, if you see a sport live, double your score and you can get your I-Spy badge more quickly.

I-SPY TITLES AVAILABLE:

SPRINT

Sprint distances are from 60m (indoors) up to 800m (two circuits of a 400m track). Running competitions were organised in ancient Egypt as far back as 6,000 years ago.

I-SPY points: 5 for each type

Date: _____

HURDLES

Hurdling is a sprinting event, over distances from 100m to 400m, in which the athletes leap the hurdles without breaking stride in their running.

True or False - A competitor is disqualified for knocking over a hurdle?

I-SPY points: 15 Double with answer

Date: _____

I-SPY points: 20

Date:

RACE WALKING

Race walking is a long-distance event, generally over 20km and 50km. Walkers must not lose contact with the ground at any time – this means that one part of the athlete's foot must be in contact with the ground at all times. This action can look very strange at first.

I-SPY points: 15

Date:

MARATHON

The 26 miles 385 yards Marathon takes its name from Marathon in Greece where the Ancient Greeks won a famous victory over the Persians in 490BC. The news was carried to Athens by a runner.

4

RELAY

The most common form of relay races are the 4 x 100m and the 4 x 400m. Each event is run by a team of four athletes. Each athlete runs the designated distance and passes a baton to their team mate. There are strict rules governing the passing of the baton.

I-SPY points: 15

Date:_____

STEEPLECHASE

Steeplechase events are run over 3,000m. Runners have to clear 28 ordinary hurdles or barriers and seven water jumps.

I-SPY points: 20

Date:_____

ARCHERY

There are two main kinds of archery using a long bow: field archery and target archery. Similarly there are two kinds using a crossbow: match crossbow and archery crossbow. Crossbows use bolts rather than arrows.

I-SPY points: 20 for each

Date:_____

DISCUS

Discus was one of the four events included in the Ancient Greek Olympian Games. The Romans also threw the discus which was originally a disc of metal or stone and is now of weighted wood with a metal rim.

I-SPY points: 15

Date:_____

6

RIFLE SHOOTING

There are two bores of rifle using 'standard' rifles or 'free' rifles which have grips to help hold them steady. Targets are fired at from standing, kneeling and lying positions.

I-SPY points: 20

Date: _____

PISTOL SHOOTING

Pistols may be small bore, larger bore or air pistols. Targets may be stationary or, in rapid-fire events, the target may appear only for a short time.

I-SPY points: 20

Date: _____

CLAY PIGEON SHOOTING

In this event the competitors use shotguns to shoot at a saucer-shaped clay target which is thrown in the air by a mechanical catapult-like device.

I-SPY points: 15

Date: _____

JAVELIN

The javelin is around 2.5m in length and has to be thrown, over arm following a short run up.

I-SPY points: 10

Date: _____

POLE VAULTING

Pole vaulting involves using a long, springy pole to propel the athlete over a high bar. Pole vaulters nowadays regularly achieve heights approaching 6m (over 19ft).

I-SPY points: 15

Date: _____

HIGH JUMP

Virtually all high-jumpers now use a technique known as the Frosbury Flop, named after Dick Frosbury who won the gold medal at the 1968 Mexico Olympic games.

I-SPY points: 10

Date: _____

LONG JUMP

Athletes sprint down a rubberised running track before jumping as far as they can from a board containing a foul line. Jumping with any part of the foot over the foul line is an illegal jump. The men's world record of 8.95m (29.4ft) has stood since 1991.

Who holds the mens world record?

I-SPY points: 10
Double with answer

Date: _____

TRIPLE JUMP

Like the long jump, competitors sprint down a track before performing a hop, skip and jump routine. This technique allows the athlete to clear huge distances. Jonathan Edwards broke the world record in 1995 with a jump of 18.29m – a record that still stands today.

I-SPY points: 15

Date: _____

9

SHOT PUT

Putting the Shot is the fourth Olympian throwing event. The men's shot, a metal ball, weighs 7.26kg (16Ib) while the women's shot is a little lighter.

I-SPY points: 15

Date:

HAMMER

Today's hammer consists of a 16Ib (7.26kg) metal ball attached to a grip by a wire. The competitor uses a spinning action from inside a safety cage to throw the hammer as far as possible.

I-SPY points: 15

Date:

WRESTLING

One of the earliest forms of martial arts, wrestling underwent a transformation in the late 20th century due to the popularity of the WWF (World Wrestling Federation – now World Wrestling Entertainment).

I-SPY points: 15

Date: _____

BOXING

Boxing is thought to have originated as a sport some 3,500 years ago in Ancient Greece. The amateur sport, in which the boxers wear vests, shorts, head protection and use large gloves, is set over three rounds. Professional boxers wear smaller gloves, no vests, no head protection and are over more rounds.

I-SPY points: 15

Date: _____

JUDO

Based on another Japanese martial art, Jujitsu, Judo was devised towards the end of the nineteenth century. It is one of the less violent and more sporting events. Experts learn to use an opponent's weight to overcome him or her.

I-SPY points: 15

Date: _____

FENCING

Originating from times when men fought battles with swords, the modern sport uses three kinds of weapon: the light foil, the slightly heavier epee, and the sabre which has cutting edges as well as points.

I-SPY points: 20

Date: _____

KARATE

Although not an Olympic sport, karate became a world-wide phenomena is the 1970s following its use in several Hollywood blockbusters and continues to be a hugely popular form of martial arts.

I-SPY points: 15

Date: _____

TAEKWONDO

Taekwondo is the national sport of South Korea and is a modern martial art that is characterised by its fast, high and spinning kicks.

I-SPY points: 15

Date: _____

RINGS

The rings are suspended from the ceiling of the gymnasium by ropes The male gymnast must carry out various swinging and holding exercises which require strength and grace.

I-SPY points: 15

Date: _____

PARALLEL BARS

Unlike the asymmetric bars of the women's event, the men's parallel bars are at the same height. There is more emphasis on strength in the positions which must be held.

I-SPY points: 15

Date: _____

ASYMMETRIC BARS

This women's gymnastics event involves the competitor carrying out graceful swinging and circling movements which must show good use of the two bars which are parallel but at different heights. The mens event is on a single bar.

I-SPY points: 15

Date: _____

BEAM

The balance beam is 5m (16ft 3in) long and only 10cm (4in) wide. Female gymnasts must carry out a linked series of turns, balances, jumps, and somersaults which require strength, grace, balance and co-ordination.

I-SPY points: 15

Date: _____

FLOOR

Individual men and women compete in floor exercises although the men's event is not performed to music. Both events combine acrobatic skills with strength and grace.

I-SPY points: 15

Date: _____

HORSE

There are two types of horse: the vaulting horse, used by both men and women, and the pommel horse, which has two rings or pommels set into the centre and is only used in mens events.

I-SPY points: 15
Double for both

Date: _____

FOOTBALL (SOCCER)

The formal name for soccer is association football. The game was played in England from as early as the fourteenth century but ball-kicking games existed at least 2,000 years before that.

I-SPY points: 5

Date: _____

GOLF

The 'official' home of golf is the 'Royal and Ancient' club at St. Andrews on the east coast of Scotland, but a similar game may have been played in China several centuries before the birth of Christ to 4,000 years ago. Mary Queen of Scots was a keen golfer.

True or False?

I-SPY points: 10
Double with answer

Date: _____

AMERICAN FOOTBALL

American football was first played in such American universities as Harvard and Yale in the nineteenth century. Clearly, its origins lie in the British sports of football (soccer) and rugby football.

How many players are there in an American Football team?

I-SPY points: 15

Double with answer

Date: _____

AUSTRALIAN FOOTBALL

This game is played on a pitch similar in shape to that of cricket. Goals are scored by kicking between goalposts, and the ball may be kicked, punched, or carried provided it is bounced every 10m (33ft).

I-SPY points: 35

Date: _____

CRICKET

Although its origins may go back to the thirteenth century, the home of the modern game is usually believed to be the village of Hambledon in Hampshire which by the late 1700s was the foremost cricket club in England.

I-SPY points: 10

Date: _____

LAWN BOWLS

Played indoors or out on a flat surface divided into rinks. Bowls are made from a solid plastic material shaped on one side such that they follow a curved line when rolled towards the jack. Teams consist of 1,2,3 or 4 bowlers who gain shots by getting nearer the jack than their opponents. Crown Green Bowls is also played in some parts of the country.

I-SPY points: 15

Date: _____

TEN-PIN BOWLING

Ten-pin bowling was developed in the United States. The ball is large and heavy with three finger holes for grip. Each player has two attempts to knock down the ten pins in each set.

I-SPY points: 20

Date: _____

I-SPY points: 20

Date: _____

VOLLEYBALL

Volleyball was created in America at the end of the nineteenth century as a game more suited to those who found basketball too demanding. It may be played indoors or out and the idea is to prevent the ball from touching the ground.

19

NETBALL

Although netball is based on the American game of basketball, the rules of the modern game, which is played mainly by women, were drawn up in England at the beginning of this century.

I-SPY points: 15

Date: _____

RUGBY FOOTBALL

There are two types of rugby played in the United Kingdom; Rugby Union, with 15 players per side is generally the most common form but Rugby League, with 13 players per side, mainly played in the north of England, is also popular. William Webb Ellis, a student at Rugby School in 1823 is generally credited with the games invention, although a format of the sport is known to have existed for many years before that.

I-SPY points: 10

Date: _____

BASEBALL

Another ball game from the United States, baseball gets its name from the four bases at the corners of the marked-out diamond shape which is the course around which the hitter (batter) must run.

I-SPY points: 20

Date: _____

BASKETBALL

It is believed that a game similar to modern basketball was played in the Central American country of Mexico as early as the tenth century.

Basketball players must not move when they have the ball. True or False?

I-SPY points: 15
Double with answer

Date: _____

21

HANDBALL

Team handball is a goal-scoring game in which the players must not touch the ball with their feet or even the lower parts of their legs.

I-SPY points: 20

Date: _____

HOCKEY

The game of hockey may have originated in Ancient Egypt more than 4,000 years ago. The name 'hockey' was first used in the nineteenth century and may come from a old French word for

what?

I-SPY points: 10
Double with answer

Date: _____

LACROSSE

There are various legends to explain the origins of this game, but its objective is to throw the ball into the opposing team's goal net using a stick with a mesh pouch at the end.

I-SPY points: 15

Date: _____

HURLING

Hurling is mainly an Irish game which is similar to hockey except that the ball may be carried on the stick as well as struck. It may even be hit with the hand or kicked.

I-SPY points: 20

Date: _____

TENNIS

Lawn tennis developed from Real Tennis, but the first club was not founded until the second half of the nineteenth century in Leamington Spa, England. The game is now played on various surfaces including tarmac, concrete and clay.

I-SPY points: 10

Date:_____

REAL TENNIS

Originally played in medieval French monastery courtyards, real tennis is played in a walled court, and the players score points by aiming the ball so that it strikes particular areas on the walls.

True or False - the other name of Real Tennis is ..... Tennis?

I-SPY points: 25
Double with answer

Date:_____

BADMINTON

Competitive badminton is played indoors on a court (although it can be played outdoors for fun). This is because the shuttlecock would be affected by the wind if used outdoors.

I-SPY points: 15

Date: _____

SQUASH

The name of this game probably comes from the fact that, in the mid-1900s, boys of Harrow School would knock up in preparation for a game of squash racquets by hitting a 'squashy' or softer ball against a wall.

I-SPY points: 15

Date: _____

TABLE TENNIS

Legend has it that the game of table tennis began at Cambridge University when some students invented a game in which they hit champagne corks across a table using cigarette packets as bats.

I-SPY points: 15

Date: _____

TRIATHLON

Triathlon races are a combination event consisting of swimming, cycling and running. Events are held consecutively and can vary in distance. Olympic distances races are 1.5km swim, 40km bike ride and 10km run. The Ultra Triathlon (or Ironman) is a staggering 3.8km swim, 180km bike ride and a full marathon!.

I-SPY points: 20

Date: _____

BUNGEE

Modern Bungee jumping has been considered a sport since it was first seen in Bristol, England in 1979. Jumpers leap from tall structures, typically a building, bridge or crane but jumps have also been made from hot-air balloons and helicopters.

I-SPY points: 15

Date: _____

ROCK CLIMBING

With major advances in the quality of ropes, boots, and other equipment, rock climbing is a much safer sport than it once was but it important to be supervised when you first start.

Who led the first successful ascent of Mount Everest in 1953?

I-SPY points: 15
Double with answer

Date: _____

POTHOLING

Otherwise known as caving or spelunking, potholing is a modern sport although there are records to show that people did descend deep into cave systems as early as the eighteenth century.

I-SPY points: 25

Date: _____

SAND BOARDING

Similar to snowboarding except that kitesurfing takes place of sand dunes and not on snow and ice!

I-SPY points: 15

Date: _____

KITESURFING

Kitesurfing has recently seen a huge growth in popularity. Kitesurfers use a large kite and board, using the wind to power them, to ride across the water, whilst at the same time performing freestyle jumps, tricks and board grabbing.

I-SPY points: 20

Date: _____

GLIDING

Gliders or sailplanes may be flown in races against the clock over triangular courses which are marked out by suitable landmarks on the ground. They are towed up in the air by a winch or aeroplane.

I-SPY points: 20

Date:

HOT AIR BALLOON

Normally seen as a idyllic way to view the countryside, balloon races' test accuracy and skill, not speed. Pilots are required to drop markers on designated targets.

I-SPY points: 15

Date:

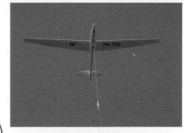

PARACHUTING

For most people, parachuting, or skydiving, is a charitable event, involving tandem jumping out of an aeroplane at heights of around 4,000m (13,000ft).

I-SPY points: 20

Date:

I-SPY points: 20

Date: _____

BILLIARDS

The game of billiards is played on a baize-covered table using only three balls, one cue ball for each of the opponents and a red ball. Points are scored by potting the red ball and by potting the opponent's cue ball by cannoning off the red ball. The two white cue balls are differentiated by one of them having a tiny black spot.

SNOOKER

It is thought that snooker got its name from the slang word used in the army to describe a new cadet. The game was invented in the 1870s by officers in the British Army in India.

I-SPY points: 10

Date: _____

DARTS

Competition darts is usually played from a starting score of 501 which is reduced as the players score single, double, treble numbers or outers (25) and bulls (50). To win a player must finish on double.

I-SPY points: 10

Date: _____

CHESS

Falling between a sport and a game, chess, or a variation of it has been played for over a thousand years. A seemingly easy game to play, it can take a life time to master! This is the original war game with kings, queens and armies.

I-SPY points: 10

Date: _____

Michelin has always embraced sport and competition – as a way of testing and developing products, as well as showcasing their technical advantages.

This was clearly illustrated in 1891, when Michelin's newly invented detachable pneumatic tyre was fitted to the British-made Humber bicycle of Charles Terront, for the 1,196km (743miles) Paris-Brest-Paris cycle race – the sternest test of man and machine. Not only were the tyres a success but Terront won the race (in the time of 71 hours and 22 minutes), and started Michelin on a road that would revolutionise the tyre industry.

As transport and competition developed, Michelin's innovative ideas were put to good use on all types of vehicle, particularl bicycles, motorcycles and cars. Whether in the Tour de France, where riders can exceed speeds of 100kph (62mph) while descending

Alpine passes; on the super-long 5km Mulsanne Straight of the famous Le Mans circuit where cars have exceeded 400kph (250mph); or in the intense heat of the North African deserts in the Dakar Rally; Michelin has created tyres that deliver performance even under the most extreme conditions.

Michelin continues to embrace the challenges that competition brings and the solutions developed find their way into the tyres that everyday road users purchase. It is on this basis that Michelin was founded and the reason why it has developed into the worldwide company that it is today.

There are various kinds of Motor Racing, the best known is probably the Formula 1 championship but there are many others.

FORMULA 1

Formula 1 is the pinnacle to which most racing drivers and manufacturers aspire. F1 started life as a Grand Prix Championship, which many car makers entered to show off their cars. Today some manufacturers have teams, but there are also independent teams. Races are usually held on specially made circuits varying in length from 2 to 4 miles. One of the most famous is in Monaco, where cars race on the streets of Monte Carlo. The season usually starts in March and finishes in October or November.

I-SPY points: 10

Date: _____

GP2

GP2 series was introduced in 2005 following the discontinuation of Formula 3000. Teams use the same chassis, engine and tyre supplier, making GP2 a true test of driver ability. Races are usually held as support races at F1 weekends. Many drivers have used GP2 as a stepping stone into F1.

I-SPY points: 20

Date: _____

GO KART

The karts have no bodywork and have small tyres which are the only form of suspension. The small engine situated behind the driver's seat combined with the light weight of the kart gives a high power ratio. These little machines can really move!

I-SPY points: 15

Date: _____

LE MANS

The world's oldest sports car endurance race was first staged in 1923 in the French town of Le Mans. The event lasts a full day and night and each car usually has three drivers. British cars have a great tradition with this event and many people travel to France each June to watch the spectacle.

I-SPY points: 40

Date:_____

FORMULA RENAULT

Formula Renault is regarded as an entry-level series to motor racing. The cars have to conform to an almost identical specification, testing the driver's ability and skill. Many F1 drivers have graduated from this type of racing.

I-SPY points: 20

Date:_____

I-SPY points: 20

Date: _____

WORLD RALLY CHAMPIONSHIP

WRC is a combination of timed races and endurance stages on public roads where drivers must obey road regulations. There are usually 15-20 special 'timed' stages driven on closed roads on all kinds on surfaces. These events usually take place over three days and there around a dozen events in different countries that make up the series.

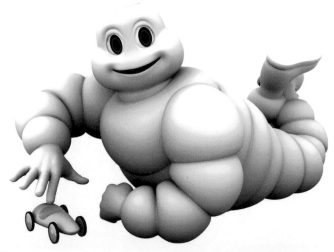

RALLY RAIDS

The most famous 'Rally Raid' is the Dakar Rally, formerly known as Paris-Dakar. This annual event for all types of off road vehicles, from trucks to cars to motorcycles, lasts up to two weeks. Originally run from Paris to Dakar in Senegal, the event now starts and finishes in many different places. The competitors can cover up to 800–900km (500–560m) each day.

I-SPY points: 20

Date: _____

DRAG RACING

Drag cars are specially designed, high-powered cars built to race from a standing start over 400m (1/4mile) in the shortest possible time. The racers compete in pairs and the cars are brought to a halt with the aid of parachutes. All the cars are different and are only designed to travel short distances in a straight line.

I-SPY points: 20

Date: _____

ROLLER SKATING

Most of the events that are performed in ice skating, such as figures, dancing, and speed skating may also be carried out on roller skates. Roller skates have the advantage of being able to be used on hard surfaces and in all temperatures, making the sport more accessible.

I-SPY points: 15

Date:

SKATEBOARDING

Skateboarders use either their own energy or the energy generated by competing in a bowl- shaped area to perform various acrobatic 'tricks' sometimes to music. The competitors are very skilful and develop their own special skills in their routines.

I-SPY points: 10

Date:

There are many forms of cycling, from recreational to racing, on road, on specially designed tracks (velodrome), and off road tracks and trails. The oldest form of cycling was on roads, and was initially designed as transport before cars and motorcycles were invented.

MOUNTAIN BIKING

Invented in California, these 'off-road' bikes are popular for all types of riding, even on roads and in cities. Specialised racing events take place in the countryside. Races vary in length and distance, but do not often last more than two to three hours. Mountain bikes have up to 30 gears to enable the riders to ride up the steepest of hills.

I-SPY points: 25

Date: _____

BMX

BMX has been the entry point for many riders into cycle racing and the skills learnt are valuable for all forms of cycle racing. BMX was huge in the 1980s and has enjoyed a resurgence following its introduction as an Olympic event. Races are very short, explosive events that require high levels of handling and tactical expertise on very short tracks. BMX bikes have one gear only.

I-SPY points: 15

Date: _____

TIME TRIALS

Time trial riders set off one minute intervals and are timed against the watch. There can be up to 120 riders in any one event; the rider with the quickest time over the set course is the winner. Races vary from 10 mile events up to 24 hour endurances when top riders cover distances of up to 500 miles. Watch out for these type of events if you are travelling about early on Sunday mornings, as these are mostly common time that they are run. Weather conditions make a difference on the result if it suddenly rains or get windy half way through the event.

I-SPY points: 15

Date: _____

TRACK RACING

This is the type of cycling that the GB Olympic team has dominated in recent years, winning many gold medals at the 2008 Olympic Games. These events are held on an indoor oval track of typically 200 - 250m that have steep banked corners so that the riders can make higher speeds around the corners. Races vary from short 'sprints' of two or three laps with two riders, to races of 200 laps (Madisons and Points Races) with more than 50 riders. Track cycles have no brakes and fixed wheel, with no gears.

I-SPY points: 15

Date: _____

CYCLE SPEEDWAY

Cycle speedway is probably the most specialised form of cycle racing. This human powered form of speedway run on flat, short oval tracks over very short distances, events are similar to BMX in that they are fast and explosive, but unlike BMX they are always run on the same shaped oval tracks. The bikes have one gear only and no brakes...........scary!

I-SPY points: 40

Date:_____

CYCLO-CROSS

Cyclo-Cross is a winter activity and uses off-road circuits where competitors both ride their bikes and carry them over obstacles. The bikes are basically road machines with small modifications to allow stronger components to be used, particularly tyres. Circuits vary from, woods, fire tracks, ploughed fields gates and even rivers.

I-SPY points: 25

Date:_____

I-SPY points: 10

Date: _____

I-SPY points: 10

Date: _____

I-SPY points: 15

Date: _____

ROAD RACES

Once referred to as Massed Start Events, riders set off together; the first to cross the line is the winner. The terrain can vary from flat courses to hilly events and distances from 30 miles up to more gruelling races of 150 miles or more for professionals. Road cycles have up to 22 gears.

STAGE RACES

Several 'road races' are linked together. The Tour de France, lasting over three weeks is one of the biggest sporting events in the world, with millions of spectators watching at the roadside and on the TV. The winner is the rider with the lowest time over the whole three weeks. The leader usually wears a yellow jersey.

SHORT CIRCUIT EVENTS

Also known as criteriums, these are usually held on circuits of one mile or less, and can be in city centres, industrial estates and even housing estates. The riders will do many laps and are usually under 40 miles.

MOTORCYCLE ROAD RACING

The most famous of these events is the Isle of Man TT held every June on a 37.75 mile road circuit. Races are held in classes depending upon the engine size and the riders set off separately and are timed over the course. Races can be up to six laps, 226 miles. In addition to these Manx events, Northern Ireland is famous for road racing, but the difference is that the riders all set off together in a 'massed start'.

What do the initials 'TT' stand for?

I-SPY points: 30

Double with answer

Date:

MOTORBIKE AND SIDECAR

Years ago the motorcycles were 'normal', with a sidecar attached. Now the motorcycles are specially made and are very low. Watch out for the passenger 'hanging' off the side of the sidecar around the corners to enable higher speeds.

I-SPY points: 25

Date:

MOTORCYCLE TRIALS

This is not a race, but specialised off road riding that tests riders skills to manoeuvre over and around obstacles. Points are deducted for the riders with the most errors (putting their foot down) and the rider with the least points wins. Tyres are very important in this technical branch of motorcycling where grip is essential.

I-SPY points: 20

Date:_____

SPEEDWAY

The best-known type of Speedway event is raced between four competitors riding 500cc motorcycles over four laps of an oval-shaped dirt or shale track. High speeds on motorcycles with no brakes – wow!

I-SPY points: 15

Date:_____

MOTOR CYCLE CIRCUIT RACING

Motorcycle circuit racing is popular in many different countries and has World series events such as Moto GP, World Superbike, as well as national and club events. Races are usually held on motor circuits and are categorised by engine size although some races ensure that riders have exactly the same type of motorbike to make the racing very close.

I-SPY points: 20

Date:

MOTO X/ENDURO

Motorcross was once better known as Motorcycle Scrambling. Machines vary mainly from 125cc to 600cc and are used to race over cross-country tracks. These bikes have specially 'knobby' tyres to provide grip on the muddy ground – make sure that you don't stand behind one as it accelerates away! Enduro bikes are very similar to Moto X events but are timed events instead of races and are over longer courses.

I-SPY points: 15 for both

Date:

ROWING

Rowing sports also include 'Sculling' in which the rower uses two oars (strictly, the word rowing should be used only to describe using one oar). The events include single sculls, pairs, fours, and eights, where there is also a cox for steering the boat.

I-SPY points: 15

Date: _____

KAYAKING

Performed over specific, often man-made courses, the competitors must manoeuvre through gates in order to complete the course in the fastest time.

I-SPY points: 20

Date: _____

SWIMMING

The main four strokes used in swimming competitions are breaststroke, butterfly, backstroke and freestyle (crawl). In Championship events, the distances range from 100m to 1500m.

I-SPY points: 10 for each stroke

Date: _____

DIVING

Competition divers are judged as they perform various somersaults, twists, and tucks of differing degrees of difficulty as they dive either from a springboard or a fixed high board into a swimming pool.

I-SPY points: 15

Date: _____

SYNCHRONISED SWIMMING

Originally know as water ballet, this is a demanding routine of moves in water, accompanied by music. Competitors can be in teams, duets or solo.

-SPY points: 20

Date: _____

47

CANOEING

Canadian canoes are broader in the beam than kayaks. In the first the paddler kneels or squats and uses a single-bladed paddle, and in the kayak, the paddler sits and uses a double-bladed paddle.

I-SPY points: 20 for each

Date: _____

WATER POLO

Water polo is a hand-ball, goal scoring game played in a swimming pool. Players may use only one hand to catch or dribble the ball and keep it for no more than 45 seconds before passing it.

I-SPY points: 20

Date: _____

SURFING

Competitors stand or kneel on specially designed surf boards, and carry out various manoeuvres as they are propelled towards the shore by the power of a breaking wave.

I-SPY points: 15

Date:

DINGHY SAILING

A sailing dinghy is a small, open sail boat usually with no permanent keel. There are many different kinds or 'classes' and various competitions for each. The word 'dinghy' comes from an Indian word meaning 'boat'.

I-SPY points: 10

Date:

RAFTING

Usually performed on rough (or white water), up to 12 people can pit their wits against nature in this thrill-seeking activity.

I-SPY points: 25

Date:

LAND YACHTING

Sometimes known as sand yachts, these wind-powered, wheeled machines may carry a crew of up to 4 people and race over sandy beaches, deserts, or on roads and old airfields.

I-SPY points: 25

Date: _____

POWERBOAT RACING

Powerboat racing has its beginnings in an event for steam-powered boats that was first held off the coast of Scotland in 1827, Nowadays, there are various classes of powerboats depending upon engine size, type of hull, etc.

I-SPY points: 15

Date: _____

COARSE FISHING

Coarse fishing or angling involves using a rod, line and hook with various kinds of bait to catch freshwater fish which do not belong to the salmon family.

I-SPY points: 10

Date: _____

FLY FISHING

In fly fishing or game fishing the person also uses a rod, hook, and line but the aim is to catch fish of the salmon family using various kinds of fly-like lures that look like food to the fish. In dry fly fishing, the 'fly' is designed to float.

What is a 'Wet Fly' designed to do?

I-SPY points: 20
Double with answer

Date: _____

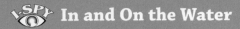

JET SKI

Jet skis are almost motorcycles in the water. They are great fun if treated correctly.

I-SPY points: 15

Date: _____

WATER SKI

Competitors are pulled behind speed boats travelling at high speed over and around obstacles.

I-SPY points: 15

Date: _____

HORSE TRIALS

Horse trials or three-day events include steeplechases over fixed fences, cross-country competitions and show jumping.

I-SPY points: 15

Date: _____

HORSE RACING

There are three main kinds of horse racing: flat racing, where there are no obstacles, hurdles, and steeple chasing where there is a mixture of hurdles, fences, ditches, and water jumps.

I-SPY points: 10 for each kind

Date: _____

SHOW JUMPING

A great variety of fences, including water jumps, may be set out over indoor or outdoor courses which usually involve competitions against the clock with penalty points or 'faults' given for refusals or for knocking down all or part of the jump.

I-SPY points: 15

Date: _____

TROTTING

In this event, one horse pulls a lightweight, two-wheeled cart called a sulky or a bike. The horse moves front left leg and rear right together and so on. A similar event, called pacing, has the horse moving front left and rear left together.

I-SPY points: 20

Date: _____

54

POLO

Played on horseback, polo is a team goal-scoring game in which the wooden ball is struck using a long-handled mallet. It has its origins in India and the word 'polo' comes from a Kashmiri word meaning 'ball'.

I-SPY points: 20

Date:_____

DRESSAGE

Where the discipline of the horse is tested in an arena to show various skills.

I-SPY points: 20

Date:_____

DRIVING

Driving events, using a four-wheeled carriage and four horses, may involve trotting or walking marathons as well as competing by driving around a course in which various obstacles, such as bridges and turns, have been set out.

I-SPY points: 20

Date:_____

SKIING

Sometimes referred to as alpine skiing, the racers compete in very fast downhill or slalom events. The word SKI is Norwegian, and means 'a stick of wood'.

I-SPY points: 15

Date: _____

CROSS COUNTRY SKIING

This very gruelling type of skiing is over a varying terrain involving both uphill and downhill.

I-SPY points: 25

Date: _____

SKI JUMPING

This sport probably has its origins in Norway in the eighteenth century, There are no official records for competitors in ski jumping because the heights of the ramps and the conditions may vary from place to place.

I-SPY points: 15

Date: _____

SLED DOG RACING

Sled Dog Racing is popular in Arctic regions but is sometimes held in the snowy regions of Scotland. Between 4-12 highly trained dogs pull a competition sled in events that include sprint, mid-distance and long-distance races that can be over 1,000 miles long! There are similar events with wheeled sleds, held over snowless terrain.

I-SPY points: 40

Date: _____

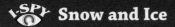

ICE SKATING

Figure skating may be performed by individual men and women as well as by pairs. Ice dancing, which is shown here, is performed only by pairs.

I-SPY points: 10

Date:

ICE HOCKEY

This game is played on ice by two teams of six players each and the aim of the game is to score by hitting a rubber disc, called a puck, into the opponent's goal which is defended by a goal keeper. A big North American sport.

I-SPY points: 15

Date:

CURLING

Interest in curling was boosted by Great Britain's gold medal success at the 2002 Winter Olympic games. Two teams each of four players slide stones across the ice toward a target area. Each team has eight stones.

I-SPY points: 15

Date:

SPEED SKATING

Speed skaters race in pairs around a track on which they change lanes after each lap. They compete over as many as six races against the clock with the winner being decided on points. Short track speed skating is where four skaters compete against each other on a small track.

I-SPY points: 20

Date: _____

SNOWBOARDING

Usually run on a similar course to slalom skiing, this new sport is gaining in popularity and is particular popular with younger competitors.

I-SPY points: 15

Date: _____

SLALOM

Where skiers test themselves against the clock on a pre-set, technical downhill course around pole markers.

I-SPY points: 10

Date: _____

TOBOGGAN

A toboggan is a lightweight sled which may be ridden by individuals or by teams of two. Luge toboggans are for one or two, but the competitors sit on them. In skeleton tobogganing, the solo rider lies face down.

I-SPY points: 25

Date:

BOBSLEIGH

Bobsleigh racing developed from an uprated luge sled. Teams of two or four individuals compete in timed runs in highly advanced, aerodynamic body shells. Very high speeds are achieved.

I-SPY points: 20

Date:

FRISBEE

You are most likely to see a frisbee being thrown and caught as a recreational plaything but it is recognised as a fully formed sport and even has its own International Frisbee Association (IFA).

I-SPY points: 5

Date: _____

AUNT SALLY

Aunt Sally is a game played in certain areas of Britain, in which players take turns to throw sticks at a ball, or dolly, on a short plinth.

I-SPY points: 15

Date: _____

CHEESE ROLLING

Competitors chase a Double Gloucester cheese down a steep hill in the Cotswolds village of Buckworth. The winner is the first to cross line at the bottom of the hill. A very quirky British game!

I-SPY points: 50

Date: _____

UNICYCLE

The one-wheeled cycle can be used in a variety of sports, including unicycle hockey – as seen in the picture.

I-SPY points: 30

Date: _____

GREYHOUND RACING

In this event, Greyhounds are released from starting traps and chase an electrically powered 'hare' around a circuit over distances up to 880yards (805m).

I-SPY points: 15

Date: _____

SUMO WRESTLING

Professional sumo wrestlers have a huge following in Japan where the sport is watched and enjoyed by millions of fans.

I-SPY points: 25

Date: _____

Index

First published by Michelin Maps and Guides 2010 © Michelin, Proprietaires-Editeurs 2010. Michelin and the Michelin Man are registered Trademarks of Michelin. Created and produced by Horizons Publishing Limited. All rights reserved. No part of this publication may be reproduced, copied or transmitted in any form without the prior consent of the publisher. Print services by FingerPrint International Book production – fingerprint@pandora.be. The publisher gratefully acknowledges the contribution of the I-Spy team: Camilla Lovell, Faron Watts and Ian Murray in the production of this title. The publisher also gratefully acknowledges the co-operation and assistance of the following who supplied pictures for this title: Frank Steele, elpoca, pilotgig racer, Ciaran Norris, Andrew Denny, Bob Cowan, Matthew Scarlett, Joe Taylor, Lifestyle Photography, Michelin, Real Tennis Professional Association, Daniel Steger, Dave Spengler, Robi, Manuel Rösler, International Billiard and Snooker Federation, Jeff Meade, Vickusin, Phil Sussman, Uwe Langer, newaza, aartj, snswebb, Jake Archibald, d.j.b., Bobby Deal, Julius Kusama, Photogregs, Eve Muirhead, David Fenwick, Dave Brunell, Jim Lamberson, Steve Shaffer and David Boardman. Other images in the public domain and used under a creative commons licence. All logos, images designs and image rights are © the copyright holders and are used with thanks and kind permission.

Answers: P3 Hurdles, False, **P9** Long Jump, Mike Powell (USA) who jumped 8.95M at the 1991 World Championship in Tokyo, **P16** Golf, True! **P17** American Football, 11, **P21** Basketball, False, **P22** Hockey, It may come from the French word for a shepherd's crook, hoquet, **P24** Real Tennis, False, it is Royal Tennis, **P27** Rock Climbing, Sir Edmund Hillary, **P43** Motorcycle Road Racing, Tourist Trophy, **P51** Fly Fishing, Sink.

HOW TO GET YOUR I-SPY CERTIFICATE AND BADGE

Every time you score 1000 points or more in an I-Spy book, you can apply for a certificate

HERE'S WHAT TO DO, STEP BY STEP:

Certificate

- Ask an adult to check your score
- Ask his or her permission to apply for a certificate
- Apply online to www.ispymichelin.com
- Enter your name and address and the completed title
- We will send you back via e mail your certificate for the title

Badge

- Each I-Spy title has a cut out (page corner) token at the back of the book
- Collect five tokens from different I-Spy titles
- Put Second Class Stamps on two strong envelopes
- Write your own address on one envelope and put a £1 coin inside it (for protection). Fold, but do not seal the envelope, and place it inside the second envelope
- Write the following address on the second envelope, seal it carefully and post to:

I-Spy Books
Michelin Maps and Guides
Hannay House
39 Clarendon Road
Watford
WD17 1JA

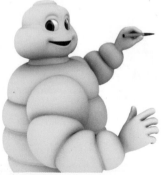